Summer Solutions.

Minutes a Day-Mastery for a Lifetime!

level 4

English Grammar & Writing Mechanics

Nancy McGraw & Nancy Tondy

Bright Ideas Press, LLC
Cleveland, Ohio

Summer Solutions Level 4
English Grammar & Writing Mechanics

Printed in the United States of America

ISBN 13: 978-1-934210-05-5
ISBN 10: 1-934210-05-6

Cover Design: Dan Mazzola
Editor: Kimberly A. Dambrogio

Instructions for Parents/Guardians

- *Summer Solutions* is an extension of the *Simple Solutions* Approach being used by thousands of children in schools across the United States.

- The 30 lessons included in each workbook are meant to review and reinforce the skills learned in the grade level just completed.

- The program is designed to be used three days per week for ten weeks to ensure retention.

- Completing the book all at one time defeats the purpose of sustained practice over the summer break.

- Each book contains answers for each lesson.

- Each book also contains the *Help Pages* which list vocabulary, parts of speech, editing marks, and rules for capitalization, punctuation, and spelling.

- Lessons should be checked immediately for optimal feedback.

- Adjust the use of the book to fit vacations. More lessons may have to be completed during the weeks before or following a family vacation.

Summer Solutions Level 4
English Grammar & Writing Mechanics

Reviewed Skills include:

- Punctuation / Capitalization

- Spelling Rules

- Editing Marks / The Writing Process

- Common and Proper Nouns / Pronouns

- Fact and Opinion

- Cause and Effect

- Verbs - Present, Past, Future / Irregular

- Adjectives

- Adverbs

- Prepositions / Prepositional Phrases

- Conjunctions / Interjections

- Synonyms / Antonyms / Homophones

- Plurals / Possessives

- Similes / Metaphors

- Commas / Quotation Marks

Help Pages begin on page 63.
Answers to Lessons begin on page 71.

Lesson #1

1. Write a contraction that can replace the underlined words.

    Jason <u>could not</u> get the car started. _____

2. Add the suffix *-ed* to change each verb to past tense.

    help -_____ cover - _____ hike - _____

3. Use the prefix *im-* to write a word that means "not polite."

    _____

4. Which of these is a fact?

    A) Coyotes usually hunt for food at night.

    B) Coyotes are more vicious than wolves.

5. Underline the conjunction that joins two phrases in this sentence.

    The girls went to the mall and to the movies on Saturday.

6. Underline two adjectives.

    Yesterday was a cold, snowy day.

7.　Underline the correct **past tense** verb.

　　Isabel had accidentally (throw / threw / thrown) the paper in the trash.

8.　Use a verb of *being* in a sentence. (is, am, are, was, were, be)

　　_____

　　_____

9.　Match these postal abbreviations with the state's full name.

　　　　TX　　　　　WV　　　　　CA

　　West Virginia _____　California _____　Texas _____

10.　A _____ takes the place of a noun.

11.　Rewrite this interjection correctly.
　　Insert a comma and an end mark.

　　Hey look at Danny's new scooter

　　_____

12.　Underline the adverb that compares.

　　Mr. Hooper has the largest tree on the street.

Lesson #2

Read this paragraph about Jane Goodall. Use it to complete items 1 – 5.

      When Jane Goodall was 26 years old, she went to East Africa to study chimpanzees. Every day Jane would try to get closer and closer to the chimps to study their behavior. One day she saw two chimpanzees take leaves off of a branch to make a tool for digging termites out of a tree. She discovered that man isn't the only one to make tools. Jane Goodall also learned that chimpanzees ate mainly fruits and vegetables, and only sometimes ate insects or small rodents. Jane was a brave and intelligent woman.

Source: HTTP://WWW.JANEGOODALL.ORG

1.   Underline the sentence that states an opinion.

2.   Circle a subject pronoun.

3.   Write the proper noun that names a place. _____

4.   What is the tense of the verbs in this paragraph?

               present   past   future

5.   What discovery did Jane Goodall make?

_____

_____

6. The word *logical* means "reasonable." What is the meaning of *illogical*?

_____

7. Circle the synonym for the underlined word.

We saw a <u>huge</u> alligator in the swamp.

   scary   angry   scaly   enormous

8. A _____ names a person, place, or thing.

9. Use the editing mark for "take something out" to fix the double negative.

I don't never want to go scuba diving again.

10. Rewrite the above sentence correctly.

_____

_____

11. Underline the prepositional phrase.

Kelly threw her graduation cap into the air.

12. Put a box around the preposition in the sentence above.

Lesson #3

1. Add commas in a series.

   Polly bought ice-cream nuts candy and cookies for the party.

2. Which words are antonyms?

   narrow   skinny   wide   tall

3. What is the root of these words?

   presentation   presentable   presented

   _____

4. Underline the conjunction.

   Dad fell on the ice but didn't break his leg.

5. Underline the object pronoun.

   Willie forgot to tell him to stop at the store.

6. Underline the adverb that tells where.

   Mark and I waited inside.

7.   Which sentence is written correctly?

      A) Now he never goes nowhere alone.

      B) Kendall can't find anything to wear.

8.   Rewrite the incorrect sentence from the item above, so that it makes sense.

_____

_____

9.   Underline the correct homophone.

Grandma lives (here / hear) during the winter.

10.   Make these nouns plural.

     child   louse   deer

_____   _____   _____

11. Always _____the first line of a paragraph.

12.   Write the titles correctly.

mr. jenkins _____   ms. kelley _____

Lesson #4

1.   Add the suffix *-less* to make a word that means "without use."

     _____

2.   about, through, under, inside, over, around, without

     What part of speech does the above list contain?

     conjunctions   adverbs   nouns   prepositions

3.   An adjective describes a noun. An adverb describes a

     _____.

4 – 5. Use two editing marks to make
       corrections in each of the sentences.

     They left the Cover off of the pool

     Did you no that tonight there will be full moon?

6 – 7. Rewrite both sentences correctly.

     _____

     _____

     _____

     _____

8 – 11. Read the paragraph. What is the part of speech of each underlined word? Write it in the proper place.

(Choose from: noun, verb, pronoun, adjective, adverb, conjunction, preposition, interjection)

Hey, do you like to use paints, chalk or clay? If so, you may want to think about becoming an artist. Artists can create original drawings or paintings. They may also draw or paint something in nature. Some artists like to work with clay. Their art is called sculpture. It takes a lot of practice to become a good artist. You may even become famous one day.

Hey ➡ _____   you ➡ _____

like ➡ _____   good ➡ _____

12. Cross out the fragment. Add some words to the fragment to make a complete thought.

Japan is an island-country in East Asia. And in the

Pacific Ocean. The capital is Tokyo. Japan has over

3,000 islands. Most of the islands have mountains.

Lesson #5

1. Which of these is a contraction?

    it's   it is   its

2. Add the suffix *-ful* to make a word that means "full of help."

    _____

3. Underline the conjunction that joins two phrases in this sentence.

    Terry went to basketball practice and
    stopped at the store on the way home.

4. Circle the common nouns in this list.

    Reggie   plane   China   marshmallow

5. Fill in a possessive pronoun that agrees
    with the subject.

    Cara brushed _____ horse this morning.

6. Underline the subject. Circle the verb.

    Mr. Torrez gave us some interesting books to read.

7.   Rewrite this sentence so that it makes sense.

Mario don't never go skiing.

_____

8.   Write the past tense forms of the irregular verb *wear*.

wear, _____, have / has / had _____

9.   Underline the sentence that states an opinion.

Mrs. Bruno read us a story after lunch.

The best stories are mysteries.

10.   Underline the cause in this statement.

There was a power failure so we had to light candles.

11.   Underline the adverb that tells when.

We had our Student Council meeting yesterday.

12.   Add quotation marks correctly.

Amanda asked, Can I borrow your camera?

Lesson #6

1.   Underline all of the adjectives in this sentence.

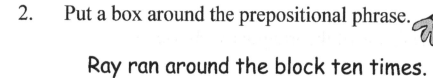

It was a bright, sunny, cool day in Cleveland.

2.   Put a box around the prepositional phrase.

Ray ran around the block ten times.

3.   Write the correct abbreviation.

Saturday - _____   December - _____   Doctor - _____

4.   Choose the correct homophone.

Nora didn't want to get her (hare / hair) cut.

5.   Underline the newspaper title.

An article in The Daily Chronicle told

about our school's new gymnasium.

6.   Insert the editing marks for "lower case" and "end punctuation" to fix this sentence.

We had Bagels and juice for breakfast

7.   Underline the main verb in this sentence. Circle the helping verb.

The wasps had stung the little girl four times.

8.   Replace the underlined word or words
with a **plural subject pronoun**.

Keesha and I are in the same homeroom.   _____

9.   Always _____ the first line of a paragraph.

Read these sentences and use them to answer questions 10 and 11.

A) Marshal did his report on insects.

B) The army private was told to report for duty.

10.   In which sentence is *report* a verb
that means "to present oneself?   A   B

11.   In which sentence is *report* a noun?   A   B

12.   Rewrite this sentence correctly.

Tyrone eight a whole watermelon at the picnic.

_____

_____

_____

Lesson #7

1. Write a contraction for *he had*.   _____

2. Which two words are synonyms?

    quick   impatient   friendly   speedy

3. Underline the conjunction in this sentence.

    There was a terrible storm, but no one got hurt.

4. Fill in commas in a series.

    Jamal has birds cats dogs turtles and
    hamsters as pets.

5. Underline the prepositional phrases in this sentence.
    Put a box around each preposition.

    Julie lives across the street

    from the library.

6. Add punctuation to this interjection.

    Ouch I hurt my hand

7 – 8.   Remember a cause tells *what happened*; an effect tells *why*.
Make up a cause and effect and write them below.

A) Cause: The thunderstorm had strong winds.

Effect: _____

B) Cause: _____

Effect: All of the students were sent home early.

9.   Underline the verbs. What is the tense of the verbs in this sentence?

Ricky will play goalie this year.

_____

10.   Which objective case pronoun can replace the underlined words?

Can you put <u>my sister and me</u> on the same team?   _____

11.   Circle the verb that is a form of *be*.

I was at the park for over two hours.

12.   Write the plural of grocery.   _____

Lesson #8

1. Underline the two things being compared in this simile.

    The sky last night was as clear as a bell.

2. Combine these into a single sentence. Write it below.

    We have cranberries for Thanksgiving dinner. We have pumpkin pie, too.

    _____

    _____

3. Underline the plural nouns.

    women   oxen   bowl   friends

4. Use the editing mark for "capitalization" to show which words should be made capital in this sentence.

    liza and marcus live on brower road.

5. Underline the adverb that tells where.

    Kendra looked everywhere for her kitten.

6. Write the editing mark for "indent." _____

7.   Underline the predicate. Circle the verb.

Jamie took a long trip.

8.   Choose the correct article.

During the meeting we were given (a/ an) light lunch.

9.   Underline the adjectives in this sentence.

Three strong horses pulled the
sleigh through the deep snow.

10 – 12.   Write a rough draft. Describe
something fun you like to do
during the winter.

_____

_____

_____

_____

_____

_____

Lesson #9

1. Replace the underlined words with a contraction.

    Harriet <u>should have</u> been there by now. _____

2. Fill in the plural subject pronoun in the second sentence.

    Mr. and Mrs. Howard left for vacation.

    _____ won't be back until next week.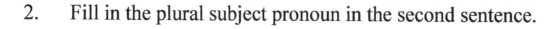

3. Write this sentence correctly.

    Last $ummer we had a (butiful)ˢᵖ rock garden⊙

    _____

    _____

4. Insert a comma and quotation marks.

    Cory asked How many more days until my birthday?

5. Underline the metaphor.

    When it comes to work, Jason is a mule.

6. Underline the helping verb.

    I am waiting to see a doctor.

7. Leon won the scholarship because <u>he had the highest grades in the class</u>. What does the underlined part of the sentence tell?

    cause　　　　　　effect

8. Cross out the fragment.

    Alaska is the largest state in size. But fewer people live there. Twice as large as Texas. Alaska has many islands.

9. Add some words to the fragment to make a complete thought.

    _____

10. Write the plural form of each noun.

    wolf ➡ _____　　city ➡ _____

11. Circle two antonyms.

    expensive　　　filthy　　　cheap　　　dirty

12. Write a sentence with a <u>future tense</u> verb.

    _____

Lesson #10

1.   Replace the underlined words with a contraction.

    I <u>could not</u> get the garage door opened. _____

2.   Underline the conjunction that joins two independent clauses in this sentence. Insert a comma before the conjunction.

    It is nine o'clock at night but it is still light outside.

3.   Underline the prepositional phrase. Circle the preposition.

    Hang your coat behind the door.

4.   What is the subject of the sentence in item #3? _____

5.   Use the editing mark for "add something" and "capitalization" to fix this sentence.

    dr. hanson is dentist.

6.   Rewrite the sentence above correctly.

_____

7. Rewrite this sentence correctly.

    There weren't no trees in our backyard.

    _____

8. Underline the metaphor.

    My dad's boss was boiling mad.

9. Which word shows *being* in this sentence?
    Circle it.

    I am the best singer in my class.

10. Underline the prepositional phrase in the sentence above.

11. Which sentence states a fact?

    A) Girls are smarter than boys.

    B) There are twelve boys in my class.

12. Underline the correct verb form in this sentence.

    I (went / goes) to the store on my way home from work.

Lesson #11

1.   Use the prefix *dis-* to write an antonym for *respected.*

      _____

2.   Double the ending consonant before adding a suffix that
      begins with a vowel.

      drop + -ed ➡ _____   bat + -er ➡ _____

3.   Underline the conjunction.

            before   until   after   so   across

4.   What are the other words in the list above?

      _____

5.   Rewrite this sentence correctly.

            I don't never get picked first.

      _____

6.   Write a contraction for *it had.*   _____

7.   Fill in an adverb to complete this sentence.

Lyn swam _____.

8.   Underline the adjectives in this sentence.

One special dog saved three lost people in the blizzard.

9.   Choose the correct article.

We found (a / an) old mirror in

(a / an) corner of the basement.

10.   Use the editing mark for "make lower case" and "take something out" to fix this sentence.

Calvin is eager to go to the the Beach.

11.   Underline the correct **past tense** verb.

Yolanda (taked / took / taken) the last seat on the bus.

12.   Circle the object pronoun.

We took him to the hospital.

Lesson #12

1. Insert a conjunction.

    Jeremy ironed his clothes, _____ he didn't
    put them away.

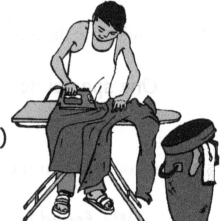

2. Underline the correct **past tense** verb.

    Jenny had (speak / spoke / spoken)
    to her teacher about the problem.

3. Choose the correct homophone.

    The ball went into (there / their / they're) yard.

4. Underline the proper nouns in this sentence.

    Mr. Wilson was our Cub Scout leader.

5. Is the word *play* used as a noun or a verb
    in this sentence?

    Our class is doing a play for the school program.

    noun   verb

6. Circle the subject. Underline the predicate.

    Playful monkeys climbed all over each other.

7.   Insert a comma and quotation marks.

Monica screamed I think I broke my arm!

8.   Look at the example. Then rewrite each noun to
      show possession.

   Example: The dog   The dog's bone is huge.

   _____ coat is new. (Kendra)

   The _____ nest fell out of the tree. (bird)

9 – 12. Complete the graphic organizer with adjectives that describe
         autumn where you live.

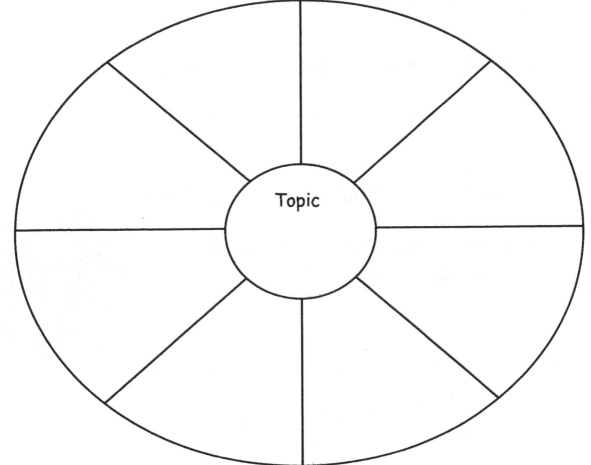

Topic

Lesson #13

1.   Form the past tense. I _____ the movie early.
                                (leave)

2.   Write the words with prefixes.

      re- + play ➡ _____   un- + do ➡ _____

3.   Underline the metaphor.

      The tiger was a bolt of lightning
      as it went after its prey.

4.   Circle the synonym for the underlined
      word.

      Cedric knew how to <u>mend</u> his torn shirt.

         clean   replace   hide   repair

5.   Underline the prepositional phrases. Circle the prepositions.

      The little boy hid under the bleachers
      for the whole game.

6.   Name the sentence type. _____

      Take off your muddy shoes.

7. Use the editing marks for "make lower case" and "check spelling" to correct this sentence.

   Wood you like to come to my House for diner?

8. Rewrite the sentence correctly.

   _____

   _____

9. A _____ takes the place of a noun.

10 – 12. Finish the chart by adding a cause or effect to each line.

Cause	Effect
It was raining.	Muriel took an umbrella to work.
	The kitchen was very cold.
The puppy was left alone too long.	
The teacher wasn't feeling well.	

Lesson #14

1. Use prefixes to write words with the following meanings.

   not buttoned _____

   write again _____

2. Underline the conjunction that joins two words in this sentence.

   George takes piano and saxophone lessons.

3. This sentence contains the title of a magazine.
   Rewrite the title correctly.

   After lunch we read the fun times.   _____

4. Read these sentences. Underline the one that states an opinion.

   Chocolate ice cream tastes better than vanilla.

   The United States eats more ice cream than any other country.

5. Fill in the **future tense** of the verb.

   Tina _____ in the program next week.
              (dance)

6. Always _____ the first line of a paragraph.

7.   Edit this sentence.

It is very dangerus to stand under a tree during a storm.

8.   Underline the plural possessive noun.

The zookeeper came to
clean the bears' cages.

9.   Underline the predicate. Circle the verb.

My parents waved good-bye from their cruise ship.

10.   Combine these sentences. Write one sentence with a
       compound verb.

The heavy ice bent the branch. The ice broke the branch.

_____

_____

11.   Choose the correct homophone.

Mom (red /read) us a bedtime story.

12.   Write the editing mark for "take something out." _____

Lesson #15

1. Add -*est* to form adjectives that compare.

    loud ➡ _____   fat ➡ _____

2. Fill in the **past tense** form of each verb.

    see ➡_____   do ➡ _____   swim ➡ _____

3. Underline the two things being compared in this simile.

    Grandma says Mark eats like a horse.

4. Rewrite this sentence correctly.

    Jamal didn't bring no books to class.

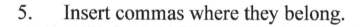

5. Insert commas where they belong.

    We are selling candy bars popcorn cookies and gum.

6. Underline the prepositional phrase.

    The dog followed us along the trail.

7.   Use the editing marks for "capitalization" and "check spelling" to make corrections to this sentence.

We went to the museum of natural history last Saterday.

8.   Underline the effect.

The little girl is crying because she lost her teddy bear.

9.   Choose the correct pronoun.

David will get the boxes for (I, me).

10.   What is the sentence type?   _____

We can't wait to go!

11 – 12. Write two sentences using any of these adjectives:

strong   tiny   angry   easy   curious   intelligent

_____

_____

_____

_____

Lesson #16

1.   Write a contraction for *we had*.   _____

2.   Underline the conjunction.

     You can take the train or the bus into downtown.

3.   Add *more* or *most* to the adjective to complete the sentence.

     Kiely is the _____ dog I know.
                       (curious)

4.   Underline two adverbs in this sentence.

     Then Mariah spoke softly.

5.   Draw a line through the fragment.

     Tropical rain forests are divided into four parts. Many

     different kinds of plants live in the rain forest. And many

     animals too. The rain forest gives us food and medicine.

6.   Rewrite the fragment as a complete thought.

     _____

     _____

7.   Circle two antonyms.

      careful   ordinary   useless   rare

8.   Make the verb show future tense.

      Next year I _____ _____ soccer.
                                    (play)

9.   Write the irregular plurals.

      thief ➡ _____

      calf ➡ _____

10.   Use the editing mark for "capitalization" and "make lower case" to
      fix this sentence.

      Casey will visit aunt sarah next Weekend.

11.   Rewrite the sentence correctly.

      _____

      _____

12.   Write a plural subject pronoun to replace the underlined words.

      Ivory and Louis are great athletes.   _____

Lesson #17

1. Look at these words. What does the prefix mean?

    prewash   preheat   preview

    _____

2. Use *-less* to write a word that means "the opposite of hopeful."

    _____

3. Insert quotation marks to correct this sentence.

    What time will you be home from work? asked Jeanne.

4. Underline the correct **past tense** verb.

    Her music lesson had (begin / began / begun) an hour ago.

5. One of the possessives in this sentence is incorrect.
    Cross it out and write it correctly on the line.

    Nicoles' brother lost his sister's watch.

    _____

6. Underline the adverb.

    Lucy carefully painted a poster for school.

7.   Underline the prepositional phrase. Circle the preposition.

Her room is down the hall.

8.   Fill in an adjective to complete this sentence.

I rode a(n) _____ horse in the parade.

9.   Write **S** if the words are synonyms. Write **A** if they are antonyms.

_____ sleepy / drowsy

_____ modern / ancient

10.   Circle the correct helping verb.

The thief (have / had) grabbed her purse.

11 – 12. Finish the chart by adding a cause or effect to each line.

Cause	Effect
	I got stung by a wasp.
I overslept.	

Lesson #18

1.   Choose the correct article.

      (A / An) ostrich can't fly.

2.   Write the two words that make up the contraction in item #1.

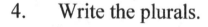

      _____   _____

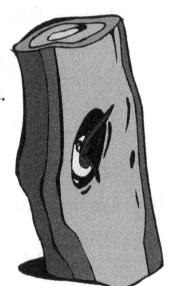

3.   Choose the possessive pronoun.

      The tree had a hole in (it's / its) trunk.

4.   Write the plurals.

      mouse ➡ _____

      city ➡ _____

5.   Circle the verb of being in this sentence.

      We were afraid of the haunted house.

6.   Use the editing marks for "end punctuation"
      and "check spelling" to fix this sentence.

      It was the bigest snow storm on record

7. Combine these two sentences to make one sentence
    with a compound predicate.

    Marsha plays softball. Marsha enjoys cooking.

    _____

8. Rewrite this sentence correctly.

    He ~~doesn't~~ never gets to go fishing.

    _____

9. Circle the verb in each set that shows **past tense**.

    invites / invited   played / will play   run / ran

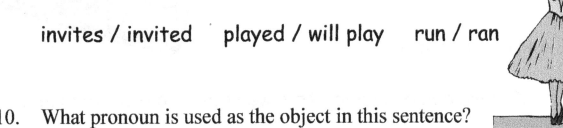

10. What pronoun is used as the object in this sentence?

    Grandma made me a turkey sandwich.   _____

11. Write a sentence that states an opinion. (Remember that an
    opinion states a personal view or belief.)

    _____

12. Underline the adverb in this sentence.

    The ballerina danced gracefully across the stage.

Lesson #19

1.   Replace the underlined words with a contraction.

      <u>It is</u> my birthday tomorrow.   _____

2.   Use editing marks to show words that should be capitalized.
      Underline the book title.

      miss grey read us the book, Charlotte's Web.

3.   Choose the correct verb.

      I (has / have) found my wallet.

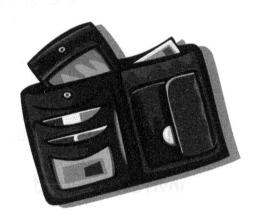

4.   Add quotation marks.

      Are we going camping this weekend? asked Monique.

5.   Insert commas where they are needed.

      Please make your bed take out the

      trash and set the table.

6.   Use the editing marks for "add something"
      and "check spelling" to fix this sentence.

      The flower had six petles and long stem.

7.   Add three adjectives to complete the sentence.

Mom bought _____ peaches, _____

cheese, and _____ milk.

8.   Are these words synonyms or antonyms?   dull / interesting

synonyms   antonyms

9 – 10.   Rewrite this run-on sentence as two complete thoughts.

We are making brownies would you like to help?

_____

_____

_____

11.   Is the underlined part of the sentence a cause or effect?

The other team didn't show up, so we won the game.

cause   effect

12.   Circle the preposition in this sentence.

Henry sat between his two friends.

Lesson #20

1. Insert commas where they are needed.

    Shauna watered the flowers cut the grass and trimmed the shrubs.

2. Write a contraction for *you had*. _____

3. Rewrite this sentence with a compound subject.

    Tamara put peppers on a pizza. Jackie put peppers on a pizza.

    _____

    _____

4. Write the abbreviation next to each month.

    November- _____ January- _____ August- _____

5. Find the subject pronoun.

    He could not find his winter boots.

6. Underline the helping verb.

    Mrs. Jackson has moved to Florida.

7.   Underline the predicate. Circle the verb.

The girls played jump rope on the playground.

8.   Choose the correct verb form in this sentence.

I (gets / got) nervous before I gave my speech.

9.   Write an adverb to complete this sentence.

Tara skated _____ through the park.

10 – 12. Write some similes of your own. Complete each of the
following.

quick as _____

pretty as _____

angry as _____

Lesson #21

1. Match these prefixes with their meanings. re- dis- pre- mis-

    "badly" ➡ _____   "before" ➡ _____

    "not" ➡ _____   "again" ➡ _____

2. Add the suffixes -er and -est to the word *long* to make adjectives that compare.

    Monday we practiced _____ than we did

    on Friday, but today was the _____

    practice of the season.

3. Insert a comma and underline the conjunction that joins two independent clauses.

    Our swim team won a trophy for diving and we almost won one for the 100 meter backstroke.

4. Underline the correct homophone.

    We had to drive in bad (whether / weather) on our way home from Florida.

5. Choose the correct **past tense** verb.

    The children (was / were / been) late for school today.

6.   Are these words synonyms or antonyms?   familiar / strange

     synonyms   antonyms

7.   Underline the prepositional phrase.
     Circle the preposition.

     The snow covered the

     tops of the mountains.

8.   Write the sentence correctly.

     I don't see nothing special about this day.

     _____

     _____

9.   Write the editing mark for "check spelling."   _____

10. Choose the correct word.

     Sarah chose the pictures (good / well).

11 – 12. Cross out the fragment. Underline the sentence with no errors.

     In science class we are studying whales. And also
     dolphins. science class is fun!

Lesson #22

1.   Use prefixes that mean "not" to write words with these meanings.

"not possible" ➡ _____ (im-)

"not agree" ➡ _____ (dis-)

2.   Underline the correct **future tense** verb.

Kelsey (march / marched / will march) in the parade.

3.   Write this sentence correctly.

The little ~~the~~ girls enjoyed∧ pony Ride⊙
                              the

_____

_____

4.   Add a comma and quotation marks to correct this sentence.

The teacher yelled It's time to come inside!

5.   Underline the common nouns.

Michael plays basketball and tennis after school.

6.   A _____ names a person, place, or thing.

7. Match the postal abbreviations with the state's full name.

    OH   NY   AZ

    New York _____   Arizona _____   Ohio _____

8. Write the contractions.

    she has _____

    it has   _____

9. Rewrite this opinion as a fact.

    Pizza is the best food in the world!

    _____

10. Insert the correct punctuation after each interjection.

    Wow you almost got hit!   Hurray we finally won!

11. Underline the subject. Circle the verb.

    A giraffe makes low sounds.

12. An adjective describes a noun. An adverb

    describes a _____.

Lesson #23

1.   Underline two adjectives.

     Terrance rode his red bike to the new playground.

2.   Underline the verb of being in this sentence.

     My cousin is in Australia for the summer.

3.   Write the prepositional phrase in the sentence above.

     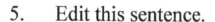

4.   Circle the conjunction in this sentence.

     My mom works at the office or at home.

5.   Edit this sentence.

     trains can either carry passengers
     or either hall supplies.

6.   Rewrite the sentence correctly.

     _____

     _____

7. Underline the correct homophone.

    The shoes were (to / two / too) small for her.

8. Underline the two things being compared in this simile.

    The snow was as white as the clouds.

9. Use the editing mark for "capitalization" to correct this sentence.

    The cat's real name is lady harrington.

10. Fill in an adverb to complete this sentence.

    Brandon _____ washed the car.

11 – 12. Finish the chart by adding a cause or effect to each line.

Cause	Effect
The road was closed.	
	I had to wait outside in the rain.

Lesson #24

1. Write a contraction for *they had*.   _____

2. Underline each independent clause in this sentence.

    Mario studied for his math test, but it was hard

    to concentrate.

3. What is the conjunction in the sentence above?   _____

4. Underline the sentence that states a fact.

    Polar bears feed only on meat.

    Polar bears are better swimmers
    than any other mammals.

5. Rewrite these as one sentence with a compound subject.

    The mayor was at the restaurant. My dentist was at the
    restaurant.

    _____

    _____

6. A _____ takes the place of a noun.

7.   Use a pronoun to replace the underlined words. _____

The police officer questioned <u>my brother and me</u>.

8.   Tell what each suffix means.

-less ➡ _____

-ful ➡ _____

9.   Circle a synonym for the underlined word.

Raking the leaves made her <u>sleepy</u>.

awake   sick   nervous   drowsy

10 – 12.   Write a rough draft. Describe some of your favorite things to
do on the weekend in 3 or 4 sentences.

_____

_____

_____

_____

_____

_____

Lesson #25

1.   Replace the underlined words with a contraction.

Mr. Ford says that <u>he is</u> getting a new kitten. _____

2.   Add some adjectives to complete this sentence.

She gave the puppy _____ water and a

_____ bone.

3.   Choose the correct article.

(A / An) baby owl is called (a / an) owlet.

4.   Use the editing marks for "check spelling" and "add something" to fix this sentence.

We are going to a pupet show morning.

5.   Write the sentence correctly.

_____

_____

6.   Write the editing mark for "capitalization." _____

7.   List five prefixes that mean "not."

_____

8.   Underline the prepositional phrase.

The little girl hid behind the door.

9.   Cross out the fragment.

Seals push themselves through the water with their rear flippers. They use their front flippers for steering. The front flippers are short. With sharp claws.

10.   Add some words to the fragment to make a complete thought or combine it with another sentence.

_____

11.   Underline the **possessive pronoun** in this sentence.

The baby seal laid by its mother until dark.

12.   Insert a comma where one is needed.

Nick asked "Can I stay up late tonight?"

Lesson #26

1.   Write the contraction for "would not." _____

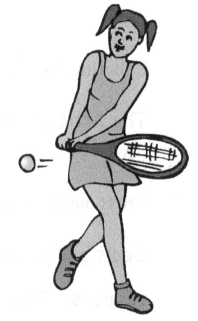

2.   Make these singular nouns plural.

     leaf ➡ _____

     box ➡ _____

     sheep ➡ _____

3.   Insert a comma and a conjunction.

No one answered the phone _____ I left a message.

4 – 5. Choose the correct pronoun.

Kendra and (I / me) like to play tennis.

The coach showed (I / me) how to improve my backhand.

6.   Use two editing marks to fix this sentence.

My mom thinks i spend to

much time reading.

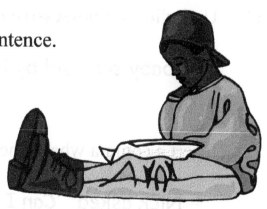

7.   Underline the adjectives in this sentence. Draw an arrow to the noun it describes.

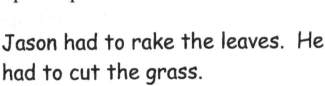

   Holly gave the puppy crunchy kibbles in a clean dish.

8.   Rewrite these as one sentence with a compound predicate.

   Jason had to rake the leaves. He had to cut the grass.

   _____

   _____

9.   Insert commas where they belong.

   No I haven't brushed my hair.

   Well you should brush it now, so we can go.

10.   Circle the conjunction in one of the sentences in item #9.

11.   Choose the correct helping verb.

   Mom (has / have) wrapped the leftovers in waxed paper.

12.   **Always** _____ **the first line of a paragraph.**

Lesson #27

Read the paragraph. Below, write the name of each part of speech that is underlined.

noun   pronoun   verb   adjective   conjunction   preposition

The <u>jaguar</u> is one of the most <u>mysterious</u> animals in
      1.   2.

nature. Jaguars have beautiful spotted fur, broad heads, and

powerful jaws. <u>They</u> prefer to live <u>in</u> forests or swamps.
                 3.   4.

Jaguars <u>are</u> meat eaters <u>and</u> usually live to be 12 – 16 years old.
        5.   6.

1.

2.

3.

4.

5.

6.

7. Underline the future tense verb.

    Janice will shop for groceries tomorrow.

8. Underline the effect.

    The school was closed because there was no electricity.

9. Write a sentence that states an opinion.

    _____

    _____

10. Write **C** for common or **P** for proper next to each noun.

    ___ Carter   ___ bank   ___ South America

11 – 12. Write two sentences using any of these adjectives.

    wonderful, interesting, friendly, strong, funny, many

    _____

    _____

    _____

    _____

Lesson #28

1.   Insert a conjunction.

      Leon's favorite foods are pizza _____ spaghetti.

2.   Write the contractions.

          we are   _____

          you are   _____

          they are _____

3.   Write a sentence of your own, using one of the contractions.

      _____

4.   Write **S** if the words are synonyms. Write **A** if they are antonyms.

      ____ hurry / rush   ____ rarely / frequently

5.   Underline the adjectives.

      Many children wore red tee-shirts for Valentine's Day.

6.   Write the verb from the sentence above. _____

Read each of the following lines and decide if the underlined parts are correct. If there is a mistake, choose the correction below the line. If there is no mistake, choose "correct as is."

7.   <u>Me and Josh</u> are on the same football team.

    A) Josh and me   B) Josh and I   C) correct as is

8.   My dad <u>has took</u> us to every game.

    A) has taken   B) taked   C) correct as is

9.   <u>Joshs mom</u> usually brings cookies for everyone.

    A) Joshs' mom   B) Josh's mom   C) correct as is

10.   His mom <u>said You</u> boys eat like horses!"

    A) said, "You   B) said, "you   C) correct as is

11.   She always <u>runs</u> out of cookies.

    A) run   B) have run   C) correct as is

12.   Make this word plural.

    church ➡ _____

Lesson #29

1.   Underline the prepositional phrases.

    We took a walk along the beach after dark.

2.   Choose the correct **past tense** verb.

    All of the fish have (swim / swam / swum)
    away from the boat.

3.   Write this sentence correctly.

    Willie and <u>m</u>arcus left (they're) lunch at home.
                          sp

_____

4.   Underline two adverbs in this sentence.

    Please completely erase the answer

    and write neatly on the line.

5.   Choose the correct homophone.

    He accidentally (threw / through) the ball
    (threw / through) the window.

6.   Write the editing mark for "add something."   _____

7. Insert commas where they are needed.

    Yes I will loan you some money.

    Well let's go shopping.

8. Underline the predicate. Circle the subject.

    The children saw tiny crabs running through the sand.

9. What is the adjective in the sentence above? _____

10. Write this run-on as two complete sentences.

    We tied up the boat a big storm was coming.

    _____

    _____

11. Write the abbreviation for each month.

    November _____   October _____

12. Underline the verb of being.

    Veronica is a nurse at the city hospital.

Lesson #30

1. Choose the correct verb form to complete the sentence.

    Black bear and coyote (live / lives) in the area.

2. Underline two things being compared in this metaphor.

    The umbrella was a roof over her head.

3. Insert quotation marks.

    Barbara asked, Has anyone seen my slippers?

4. Choose the correct homophone.

    Rhonda says I worry (to / two / too) much.

5. Underline the nouns that are plural.

    patches   children   toy   oxen   couch

6. Use the editing marks for "add something" and "check spelling" to correct this sentence.

    The baseball flu high over fence.

7. Add an adverb to complete this sentence.

    Ricky _____ studied for his test.

8. Add an apostrophe to make these plurals possessive.

    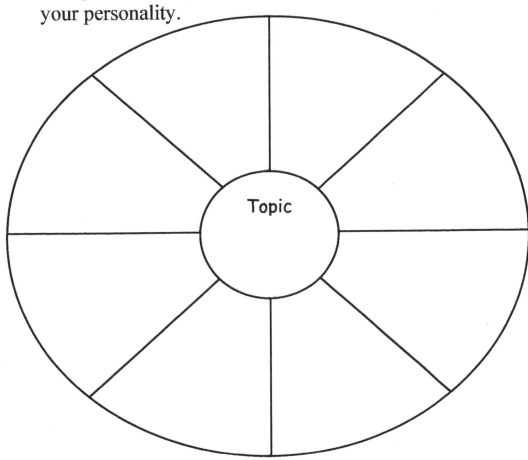

    Don't bump into the birds____ nest!

    The girls____ sweaters were all over the floor.

9. Write the plural subject pronouns below.

    _____   _____   _____

10 – 12. Complete the graphic organizer with adjectives that describe
          your personality.

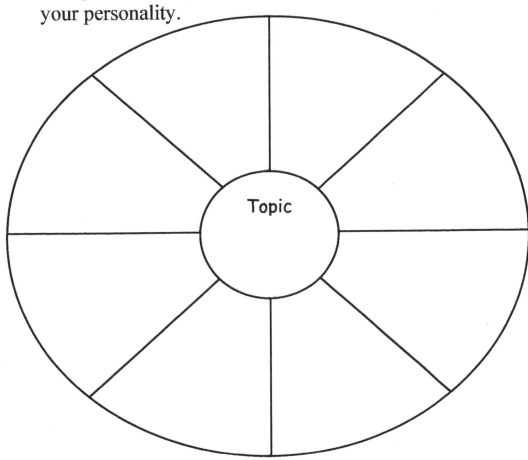

Topic

level 4

English Grammar
& Writing Mechanics

Help Pages

Help Pages

Vocabulary:	
Sentence	a group of words that tells a complete thought
Subject	tells who or what the sentence is about
Predicate	tells what the subject does or is
Synonym	a word that means the same or almost the same as another word
Antonym	a word that means the opposite of another word

Homophones, homonyms, and **homographs** are words that sound alike or are spelled alike (or both), but have different meanings. This chart will help you remember which is which.

	Homonyms	Homographs	Homophones
Spelling	same	same	different
Pronunciation	same	different	same
Meaning	different	different	different

Editing Marks:	
Capital letter	≡
End Punctuation	⊙ ! ?
Add Something	∧
Change to lower case	/
Take something out	ℐ
Check Spelling	*sp* ⬭
Indent	¶

Helping Verbs:		
is	can	may
are	could	might
am	should	have
was	would	has
were	will	had
	shall	

Help Pages

Parts of Speech:		
Noun		a word that names a person, place, or thing
Verb		a word that shows action or a state of being; a verb is the main word in the predicate
Pronoun		a word that takes the place of a noun
Adjective		a word that describes a noun; an *article* is a special type of adjective; the only 3 are *a, an, the*
Adverb		a word that describes a verb (often ends in *-ly*)
Conjunction		a word that connects words or phrases in a sentence (and, or, but, so)
Preposition		a word that relates a noun or pronoun to other words in a sentence (see list); a <u>prepositional phrase</u> begins with a preposition and ends with noun or pronoun
Interjection		a word or short phrase that shows emotion (Wow! Aha! Oh no!)

Prefix	meaning
un-, dis-, im-, in-, ir-, il-	not
re-	again
mis-	badly
pre-	before

Forms of the Verb Be:		
Present	Past	Future
am	was	will be
is	were	
are		

Kinds of Sentences:		
Declarative	a <u>statement</u>; tells something	.
Interrogative	a <u>question</u>; asks something	?
Imperative	a <u>command</u>; tells someone to do something	.
Exclamatory	an <u>exclamation</u>; shows emotion	!

Help Pages

Steps in the Writing Process:	
1. Prewriting	getting ideas for writing
2. Drafting	putting your ideas into writing
3. Revising	adding or taking out to make your writing better
4. Editing	using editing marks to correct mistakes
5. Publishing	sharing your writing with others

Spelling Rules:
1. Words ending in *s, x, z, ch,* or *sh,* add *–es* to make the plural.
2. If a word has only one syllable or just one vowel, <u>double the ending</u> <u>consonant</u> before adding *–er or –est.*
3. To make compound words, usually join two words without changing the spelling of either word.
4. When adding a suffix to a word, the spelling of the word sometimes changes; the suffix does not usually change.
5. If a word ends in *–e* and you want to add a suffix that begins with a vowel, drop the *–e* before adding the suffix.
6. When a word ends in a consonant + *y,* change the *y* to *i* and add *–es.*

Rules for using **Quotation Marks:**
1. Put quotation marks before and after the actual words that someone says. Think of quotation marks as the frame around spoken words. Keep the end mark inside the quotes. Example: "Here comes Lila!"
2. Use a comma before or after a quote within a sentence. Examples: Laura exclaimed, "What a beautiful song!" "Let's get some ice cream," said Jack.
3. Do not use a comma at the end of the quote if there is another punctuation mark. Example: "Grandma's here!" exclaimed Sasha.

Help Pages

Rules for using **Commas**:
1. Use commas to separate words or phrases in a series. Example: I'll take a dozen eggs, a watermelon, two loaves of bread, and a ham.
2. Use a comma to separate two independent clauses joined by a conjunction. Example: He has red hair, and she has gray hair.
3. Use a comma after an introductory word, such as an interjection. Example: Hey, where are you going? Do not use a comma if there is an end mark after the interjection. Example: Look! There it is.
4. Use a comma to separate two words or two numbers, when writing a date. Example: Monday, February 20, 2010

Pronouns:		
Type	**Singular**	**Plural**
Object Pronouns (or Objective Case Pronouns) are found in the predicate of a sentence.	me, you, him, her, it	us, you, them
Subject Pronouns (or Nominative Case Pronouns) are used as the subject of a sentence or clause.	I, you, he, she, it	we, you, they
Possessive Pronouns are used to show possession. These possessive pronouns modify a noun.	my, your, his, her, its	our, their, whose
**These possessive pronouns are used alone.	mine, yours, his, hers	ours, theirs, whose

Cause and Effect	An **effect** tells *what* happened. A **cause** tells *why* it happened. (Some clue words for a cause/effect relationship are: *because, therefore, so, since.*)
Fact verses Opinion	A **fact** can be proven. An **opinion** states a belief or feeling.

Help Pages

Plagiarism	<u>Plagiarism</u> is the illegal use of another person's words, putting your name on someone else's work, copying another person's words or work, or not giving credit to a source.
Abbreviations	An <u>abbreviation</u> is a shortened form of a word. Some abbreviations, such as social titles, months and weekdays, end in a period. Examples: Dr. Mr. Ms. Mrs. Sept. Feb. Mon. Thurs. Postal abbreviations do not end in a period. AK OH PA WV

Figures of Speech:	
Simile	A <u>simile</u> is a way to describe something by using a comparison. A simile compares two things using the words *like* or *as*. Example: My sister is *as stubborn as a mule*. (My sister is being compared to a mule.)
Idiom	An <u>idiom</u> has a special meaning in a certain language. It is not a literal meaning. For example, in America we say, "She is always willing to *go the extra mile*." This statement has nothing to do with going anywhere. It means someone is a hard-worker or is willing to do extra work.
Metaphor	A <u>metaphor</u> compares two things but does not use *like* or *as*. It uses a form of the verb *be*. Example: He *is a tiger* on the field!

Verb Tenses:	
Present Tense Verbs	Most present tense verbs end in -*s* when the subject is singular. Examples: He runs. They run.
Past Tense Verbs	These verbs tell an action that has already happened. Regular verbs usually add -*ed* to show past time.
Future Tense Verbs	These verbs describe an action that is going to happen. Add the helping verb *will* to show future time.

Help Pages

Irregular Verbs:		
Present	**Past**	**With *has*, *have*, or *had***
am / is / are	was / were	*has, have,* or *had* been
begin	began	*has, have,* or *had* begun
blow	blew	*has, have,* or *had* blown
break	broke	*has, have,* or *had* broken
bring	brought	*has, have,* or *had* brought
choose	chose	*has, have,* or *had* chosen
drive	drove	*has, have,* or *had* driven
fly	flew	*has, have,* or *had* flown
freeze	froze	*has, have,* or *had* frozen
make	made	*has, have,* or *had* made
ring	rang	*has, have,* or *had* rung
say	said	*has, have,* or *had* said
sing	sang	*has, have,* or *had* sung
speak	spoke	*has, have,* or *had* spoken
steal	stole	*has, have,* or *had* stolen
swim	swam	*has, have,* or *had* swum
tear	tore	*has, have,* or *had* torn
tell	told	*has, have,* or *had* told
think	thought	*has, have,* or *had* thought
throw	threw	*has, have,* or *had* thrown
wear	wore	*has, have,* or *had* worn

Some Common **Prepositions:**					
about	around	by	in	on	to
above	before	down	inside	out	under
across	behind	during	into	outside	until
after	below	except	near	past	up
along	beside	for	of	through	with
among	between	from	off	throughout	without

level 4

English Grammar
& Writing Mechanics

Answers to Lessons

	Lesson #1		Lesson #2		Lesson #3
1	couldn't	1	<u>Jane was a brave and intelligent woman.</u>	1	Polly bought ice cream, nuts, candy, and cookies for the party.
2	helped hiked covered	2	(she)	2	narrow wide
3	impolite	3	East Africa	3	present
4	A	4	past	4	<u>but</u>
5	<u>and</u>	5	Man isn't the only one to make tools.	5	<u>him</u>
6	<u>cold</u> <u>snowy</u>	6	not reasonable	6	<u>inside</u>
7	<u>thrown</u>	7	(enormous)	7	B
8	Answers will vary.	8	noun	8	Now he never goes anywhere alone. Answers may vary.
9	West Virginia – WV California – CA Texas - TX	9	never or don't	9	<u>here</u>
10	pronoun	10	I don't ever want to… or I never want to…	10	children lice deer
11	Hey, look at Danny's new scooter!	11	<u>into the air</u>	11	indent
12	<u>largest</u>	12	into	12	Mr. Jenkins Ms. Kelley

	Lesson #4			Lesson #5			Lesson #6
1	useless	1	it's		1	bright sunny cool
2	prepositions	2	helpful		2	around the block
3	verb	3	and		3	Saturday – Sat. December – Dec. Doctor – Dr.
4	They left the cover off of the pool ⊙	4	plane marshmallow		4	hair
5	Did you no that tonight there will be a full moon?	5	her		5	The Daily Chronicle
6	They left the cover off of the pool.	6	Mr. Torrez gave us some interesting books to read.		6	We had Bagels and juice for breakfast⊙
7	Did you know that tonight there will be a full moon?	7	Mario doesn't ever go skiing. or Mario never goes skiing.		7	main – stung helping – had
8	Hey – interjection	8	wore worn		8	We
9	you – pronoun	9	The best stories are mysteries.		9	indent
10	like – verb	10	There was a power failure		10	B
11	good – adjective	11	yesterday		11	A
12	And in the Pacific Ocean. (Answers will vary.)	12	Amanda asked, "Can I borrow your camera?"		12	Tyrone ate a whole watermelon at the picnic.

	Lesson #7		Lesson #8		Lesson #9
1	he'd	1	<u>sky</u>　　<u>bell</u>	1	should've
2	quick　　　speedy	2	We have cranberries and pumpkin pie for Thanksgiving dinner.	2	They
3	<u>but</u>	3	<u>women</u>　<u>oxen</u>　<u>friends</u>	3	Last summer we had a beautiful rock garden.
4	Jamal has birds, cats, dogs, turtles, and hamsters as pets.	4	<u>l</u>iza and <u>m</u>arcus live on <u>b</u>rower <u>r</u>oad.	4	Cory asked, "How many more days until my birthday?"
5	across the street from the library	5	<u>everywhere</u>	5	<u>Jason is a mule.</u>
6	Ouch, I hurt my hand.　or　Ouch! I hurt my hand.	6	¶	6	<u>am</u>
7	Answers will vary.	7	Jamie (took) a long trip.	7	cause
8	Answers will vary.	8	a	8	~~Twice as large as Texas.~~
9	<u>will play</u>　future	9	<u>Three</u>　<u>strong</u>　<u>deep</u>	9	Alaska is twice as large as Texas. Answers will vary.
10	us	10		10	wolves　　cities
11	(was)	-	Answers will vary.	11	(expensive)　(cheap)
12	groceries	12		12	Answers will vary.

Lesson #10		Lesson #11		Lesson #12	
1	couldn't	1	disrespected	1	but (and, so)
2	It is nine o'clock at night, <u>but</u> it is still light outside.	2	dropped batter	2	<u>spoken</u>
3	(behind) the door.	3	<u>so</u>	3	their
4	You	4	prepositions	4	<u>Mr. Wilson</u> <u>Cub Scout</u>
5	dr. hanson is ∧ dentist. ≡ ≡ a	5	I never get picked… or I don't ever get…	5	noun
6	Dr. Hanson is a dentist.	6	it'd	6	(Playful monkeys) <u>climbed all over each</u> <u>other</u>.
7	There were no trees … or There weren't any…	7	Answers will vary.	7	Monica screamed, "I think I broke my arm!"
8	<u>boss was boiling mad</u>	8	<u>One</u> <u>special</u> <u>three</u> <u>lost</u>	8	Kendra's bird's
9	(am)	9	We found an old mirror in a corner of the basement.	9 - 12	Answers will vary.
10	<u>in my class</u>	10	Calvin is eager to go to <s>the</s> the Beach.		
11	B	11	<u>took</u>		
12	<u>went</u>	12	(him)		

	Lesson #13			Lesson #14			Lesson #15
1	left		1	unbuttoned rewrite		1	loudest fattest
2	replay undo		2	and		2	see ➡ saw do ➡ did swim ➡ swam
3	The tiger was a bolt of lightning		3	The Fun Times		3	Mark horse
4	(repair)		4	Chocolate ice cream tastes better than vanilla.		4	Jamal didn't bring... or Jamal brought no...
5	The little boy hid (under) the bleachers (for) the whole game.		5	will dance		5	We are selling candy bars, popcorn, cookies, and gum.
6	Imperative		6	indent		6	along the trail.
7	(Wood) ^sp you like to come to my House for (diner) ^sp?		7	It is very (dangerus) ^sp to stand under a tree during a storm.		7	We went to the museum of natural history last (Saterday.) ^sp
8	Would you like to come to my house for dinner?		8	bears'		8	The little girl is crying
9	pronoun		9	(waved) good-bye from their cruise ship.		9	me
10			10	The heavy ice bent and broke the branch.		10	Exclamatory
-	Answers will vary.		11	read		11	
12			12	𝒥		- 12	Answers will vary.

Lesson #16		Lesson #17		Lesson #18	
1	we'd	1	before	1	An
2	<u>or</u>	2	hopeless	2	can not
3	most curious	3	"What time will you be home from work?" asked Jeanne.	3	its
4	<u>Then</u> <u>softly</u>	4	<u>begun</u>	4	mouse ➡ mice city ➡ cities
5	~~And many animals too.~~	5	~~Nicoles'~~ Nicole's	5	(were)
6	Many different kinds of plants and animals live in the rain forest.	6	<u>carefully</u>	6	It was the (bigest) sp snow storm on record (.)
7	(ordinary) (rare)	7	(down) the hall.	7	Marsha plays softball and enjoys cooking.
8	will play	8	Answers will vary.	8	He never gets to go fishing.
9	thief - thieves calf - calves	9	<u>S</u> - sleepy/drowsy <u>A</u> - modern/ancient	9	(invited) (played) (ran)
10	Casey will visit <u>a̲unt</u> s̲arah next W̶eekend.	10	(had)	10	me
11	Casey will visit Aunt Sarah next weekend.	11 - 12	Answers will vary.	11	Answers will vary.
12	They			12	<u>gracefully</u>

	Lesson #19		Lesson #20		Lesson #21
1	It's	1	Shauna watered the flowers, cut the grass, and trimmed the shrubs.	1	badly ➡ mis- not ➡ dis- before ➡ pre- again ➡ re-
2	miss grey read us the book, Charlotte's Web.	2	you'd	2	longer longest
3	have	3	Tamara and Jackie put peppers on a pizza.	3	Our swim team won a trophy for diving, and we almost won...
4	"Are we going camping this weekend?" asked Monique.	4	Nov. Jan. Aug.	4	weather
5	Please make your bed, take out the trash, and set the table.	5	He	5	were
6	The flower had six petles and ʌ long stem. sp a	6	has	6	antonyms
7	Answers will vary.	7	The girls played jump rope on the playground.	7	of the mountains.
8	antonyms	8	got	8	I see nothing special about this day. (Answers may vary.)
9 - 10	We are making brownies. Would you like to help?	9	Answers will vary.	9	sp
				10	well
11	cause	10 - 12	Answers will vary.	11	And also dolphins.
12	between			- 12	In science class we are studying whales.

Lesson #22		Lesson #23		Lesson #24	
1	impossible disagree	1	<u>red</u> <u>new</u>	1	they'd
2	<u>will march</u>	2	<u>is</u>	2	<u>Mario studied for his math test</u>, but <u>it was hard to concentrate.</u>
3	The little girls enjoyed the pony ride.	3	for the summer or in Australia	3	but
4	The teacher yelled, "It's time to come inside!"	4	(or)	4	<u>Polar bears feed only on meat.</u>
5	<u>basketball tennis</u> <u>school</u>	5	<u>trains</u> can either carry passengers or either (hall) supplies. *sp*	5	The mayor and my dentist were at the restaurant.
6	noun	6	Trains can either carry passengers or haul supplies.	6	pronoun
7	New York – NY Arizona - AZ Ohio – OH	7	<u>too</u>	7	us
8	she's it's	8	<u>snow</u> <u>clouds</u>	8	-less ➡ <u>without</u> -ful ➡ <u>full of</u>
9	Answers will vary.	9	The cat's real name is <u>lady harrington</u>.	9	(drowsy)
10	Wow, you almost got hit! Hurray, we finally won!	10	Answers will vary.	10	Answers will vary.
11	<u>A giraffe</u> (makes) low sounds.	11 - 12	Answers will vary.	- 12	
12	verb				

Lesson #25		Lesson #26		Lesson #27	
1	he's	1	wouldn't	1	jaguar – noun
2	Answers will vary.	2	leaves boxes sheep	2	mysterious - adjective
3	A baby owl an owlet.	3	No one answered the phone, so (but) I left a message.	3	They – pronoun
4	We are going to a (pupet) show ∧ morning. sp this	4	Kendra and I like to play tennis.	4	in – preposition
5	We are going to a puppet show this morning.	- 5	The coach showed me how to improve my backhand.	5	are – verb
6	≡	6	My mom thinks i spend (to) much time reading. sp	6	and – conjunction
7	un, dis, im, in, il, ir	7	crunchy kibbles clean dish	7	will shop
8	behind the door.	8	Jason had to rake the leaves and cut the grass.	8	The school was closed
9	With sharp claws.	9 - 10	No, I haven't brushed my hair. Well, you should brush it now, (so) we can go.	9	Answers will vary.
10	The front flippers are short with sharp claws.			10	P Carter C bank P South America
11	its	11	has	11	
12	Nick asked, "Can I stay up late tonight?"	12	indent	- 12	Answers will vary.

	Lesson #28			Lesson #29			Lesson #30
1	Leon's favorite foods are pizza <u>and</u> spaghetti.		1	<u>along the beach</u> <u>after dark</u>		1	live
2	we're you're they're		2	swum		2	<u>umbrella</u> <u>roof</u>
3	Answers will vary.		3	Willie and Marcus left their lunch at home.		3	Barbara asked, "Has anyone seen my slippers?"
4	<u>S</u> hurry/rush <u>A</u> rarely/frequently		4	<u>completely</u> <u>neatly</u>		4	too
5	<u>Many</u> <u>red</u>		5	threw the ball through the window		5	<u>patches</u> <u>children</u> <u>oxen</u>
6	wore		6	∧		6	The baseball (flu)high over ∧fence. the
7	B		7	Yes, I will loan you some money. Well, let's go shopping.		7	Answers will vary.
8	A		8	The children saw tiny crabs running through the sand.		8	birds' girls'
9	B		9	tiny		9	we you they
10	A		10	We tied up the boat. A big storm was coming.		10	Answers will vary.
11	C		11	Nov. Oct.		-	
12	churches		12	<u>is</u>		12	